illuminations

The Mackinac Island Coloring Book
for Grown-Ups

Conceived by

Kristen M. Hains

and

Matt McCormick

Inspired by the photography of Matt McCormick

Illuminations: The Mackinac Island Coloring Book for Grown-Ups

Cover Design/Interior Layout by Matt McCormick

Editorial Assistant: Carol South

Additional reference photography courtesy of Carol South and Kiley Crowell

Welcome to Illuminations,
the Mackinac Island Coloring Book for Grown-Ups.

The images with fine detail and repeating patterns
are perfect for adults. For younger artists, choose a
page that features large, solid areas to color.

If you're wondering what materials
to use, the sky is the limit. Feel free
to use colored pencils, crayons, or even
markers. Gel pens work really great!
One note about permanent markers,
though. Most permanent markers are
heavy and may tend to bleed. You'll want
to do a small test to make sure this doesn't
happen or you may lose the image on the other side.

Relax, have fun, and immerse yourself
in the colorful world of Mackinac Island's charm.

ILLUSTRATIONS BY PAGE

Mackinac Island

11

12

24

33

44